Stale Bread & Miracles.

a novel in prose poetry

JAN FORTUNE-WOOD

Cinnamon Press
Independent Innovative International

Published by
Cinnamon Press
Meirion House
Glan yr afon
Tanygrisiau
Blaenau Ffestiniog
Gwynedd
LL41 3SU
www.cinnamonpress.com

The right of Jan Fortune-Wood to be identified as author of this work has been asserted by her in accordance with the Copyright, Designs and Patent Act, 1988. © 2008 Jan Fortune-Wood
ISBN 978-1-905614-98-1

British Library Cataloguing in Publication Data. A CIP

Designed and typeset in Palatino by Cinnamon Press; Cover design by Mike Fortune-Wood from original artwork: 'Mother's Day' © Mike Fortune-Wood
Printed and bound in Great Britain by Biddles Ltd, King's Lynn, Norfolk

Acknowledgements

Thanks are due to so many people that I should apologise in advance to the many not mentioned, but I am grateful to everyone who read the manuscript and offered criticism and encouragement, especially Mike Fortune-Wood, Rowan Fortune-Wood, Stella Howden, Gladys Mary Coles, Aileen La Tourette and Ann Drysdale. Thanks to Heather Burnley for the tranquillity of Ysgubor Wen where I was able to complete the first draft and to all those who kept me sane and hopeful throughout this journey—Lorna, Margaret, Rupert, Bernice, Charmion, Bryan, Gareth, Sharon, Kirsty, Jonathan, Alison, April, P.M.†, Karen, Nanik, Gaby, Mark, Louise, Angie, Neill, Tracy, Ali, Alex, Rosie, Sherry, Tom, Val, Dawn, Paul, Janet, Cyndy, Alan, Eric, Vera, Stan, Gisela, Barbara, Bill, Ann, Patricia, Michaela, Gladys, Les, Veronica, Charlie, Dr M, Dr Dawn and Louise.

Most of all thanks to my family: Mike, Rowan, Tamsyn, Cottia and Seth Fortune-Wood.

Contents

Stale Bread & Miracles:

a novel in prose poetry

Called you by your name

What we want to discern is summed up in one word: vocation and calling. As I said, one word.
Canon Lynley smiles, breathes deeply and blows, points to a jumble of words, the last one: VOCATION.

In the library, books shed dust like unread words from parchment skins, the Canon nods his white-haired head, asks to its beat, *You're how old, dear?*
From the sinking springs of an ancient chair I say I'm twenty-four.
And can you relate to adults, dear? His smile is cherubic. He nods and nods and finally adds, *Surely you'd be better off at home—having babies, dear.*

The final test, to assess my spiritual growth, is a single question at dusk: *Do you have a sense of humour, dear?*

The lost epistle

I'm ushered along whitewashed catacombs, the bowels of the diocese.
Come in! We'll go to my office.
She nods at the one uncluttered chair, spoons fair trade coffee into once-white mugs.
You must be pleased. You'll need to arrange a college place.
I blink and ask, *You mean I've passed?*
You've had the bishop's letter, Meg. I've got a copy here.
It's the first I've heard.
For goodness sake, you should have said. You must hear it from the bishop first. We haven't spoken of this today. You understand?
I acquiesce; make my way back through the passages towards the light.

Blessing on your offspring

I check that I'm alone. 8.35 a.m. Throwing up is punctual.
Glance in the mirror. Ready to meet 5N.

The call comes at half term.
*We can offer you a place this year instead of next. We're aware
that you're expecting. But you won't have many lectures. Not
with your research. You could manage with the baby. Bring him
into college. He'll be our little mascot. So everything's agreed.*

The call comes in the first week of the college term.
*There's a reason that your grant has not been paid... best
interest... For the baby's sake... We need some guarantee...
some evidence that you can cope with college and a baby... and
be a proper mother... it could reflect badly on the church...
Surely you see...*

We have a mortgage—I've given up my job—My husband
is a student—I'm eight months pregnant—I have no grant
until I prove myself a proper mother to an unborn child.

Do what you can.
The call goes dead.

Odious to the inhabitants

I wake to a distant tapping sound. Evening: a sodden Saturday in a grey November. I stretch and listen, follow the beat upstairs to where a rupture in the ceiling seeps water onto satinwood. I stare in stupor, rouse and fetch a bucket. The builder says we have a year before the roof beams split.
Rob says, *You'd better have a word with your God.*

Our Mole is born, rooting and black-haired.
A Christmas boy.

At college I'm given a room of my own to work on my thesis in feminist theology. Just me and Mole and all the students' wives who come each morning to my study, also known as 'the designated nappy changing room'.

I dread the smell of faeces in the morning.

Enough for today

I wander the house till Rob comes home. His finals loom. The roof's still caving in. I've rocked Mole off to sleep. My eyes chance on the glitzy clock Rob's father bought; its complicated face.

You see this hand? It tells the time wherever I happen to be in the world. The hand ends in a metal aeroplane. *If you had a proper job*, this for Rob, *you could buy nice things like this and a decent house, instead of living here.*

I seize the clock and hurl it at the wall. It gouges into plasterwork. I'm in my stride, stamp it into gaudy bits of mangled springs, the plane crushed to oblivion; scoop the wreckage into carrier bags.

As my RE teacher always used to say:
Today's trouble is enough for today...

Signs—

The broadsheets carry interviews with those who have *concerns*—words like *contamination* and *infection* describe the dire effect of letting women touch the holy bread. Others mourn the proper way of things—man as woman's head.

and wonders

A letter comes to say that next year's grant is cut. It tells me: *Other families just like yours manage on much less.* No-one will tell me who these other families are.

We're summoned to the diocese, told we should have moved to college rooms (the ones that had no vacancies); that travelling to college puts my mileage in excess; that Rob should find a job—

Perhaps you could sell tents, the diocesan secretary says, tapping a fat gold pen against a broad oak desk. *Supporting students' wives to stay at home with children is only natural, but you must admit that your arrangement is somewhat unusual.*

Back at home, the test is positive.

The rich shall not give more

We're summoned to a finance interview. Mole in tow, we spend an evening berated for ingratitude while I defend antiques from toddler hands.

I'm required at the bishop's palace and told to come alone; Rob's contribution has been *less than positive*.
The bishop offers me a loan.

We write to charities. The letters, by return, remind me that I'm not a proper ordinand. I lack the vital requisite— not being a man. They wish me every blessing on my ministry.

The Council is concerned that *all these babies will hinder your participation in college life.*
Mole's at home with Rob; the second baby won't be born until the final term.
Perhaps you should stay at college for an extra year—for your spiritual formation—you understand? We've arranged some interviews.

Perverse before me

So you don't have any lectures?
I nod, explain my first degree exempts me. I spend my days alone—apart from worship, lunch and visits from the nappy changing wives.
And the extra year is for?
Spiritual formation.
He gazes at the nappy bucket. Shakes his head.

The second interviewer asks, *Is he developing alright? Your little boy, I mean; being cared for by a man.*
Well he looks quite normal, don't you think? But I've read they have to be a year old before you test for sexual orientation. We're trying not to worry.
She guffaws, decides I'm spiritually formed.

Let the little children...

My tutor asks to have a word, says how good it is of Rob
to come to worship with the tutor group, how kind of him
to bring in his guitar—but: *I'm not convinced it's the place
for a one year old.* He realises several wives bring toddlers
to tutor time, but the difference is that, *your child, no
offence, tends to wander round.*
Unlike other one year olds?
He's not being difficult, only thinking of us. *Perhaps it
would be easier...*
If they didn't come?
Of course Rob's welcome, but perhaps it would be better
not to take the little one to *any* college worship...

Abstain... from fornication

At college my closest friend is male. Nick's staying on an extra year, doesn't have a study, but decides he could share mine.

You know he's married, don't you? Stage-whispers a nappy-changing wife as an anxious pair scurry from my room.

Sometimes I dread to go in there, the other says. *They're always laughing you know.*

It's delicate, says the Principal. *Nothing is being implied of course, but if it gives the wrong impression—the two of you... Anyway I've found someone who'll share his study with Nick, so he won't be needing...*

I can't return to solitary confinement in the nappy changing room. Instead I bribe Nick's room-mate with the promise of fresh coffee daily and move into their room. I'm above suspicion with two married men.

Into the wilderness

The thing is that the diocese has so few vacancies and I'm afraid your particular gifts... The Bishop has agreed to your release.
So I am set free from having a post to go to.

But the Principal has a friend—he's sure we'll click. The only thing... the parish doesn't have a curate's house. When the vicar learns we have no funds to buy one, he writes to let us know that, after all, this wasn't what God willed.

A letter from a church in York is, *sorry to disappoint, but couldn't possibly consider a working mother.* They hope I will appreciate their concern for my best interests... *Love in His Name...*

In a muddy farmyard as snow begins to fall an old man fights a rusted lock.
Excuse me we've broken down going to an interview. I wonder—could we use your phone?
Rob eyes the barking dog.
Don't mind 'im. Soft as butter 'e is.
Rob is almost to the door when the dog makes its lunge. I hear Rob yelp, see him cradle his leg.
Well, I've never seen 'im do that b'fore. Marge! Get the bromide, love.

Not my people

The interviewing couple are vicar and deacon.
Deacon-wife, two years older than me, wears flowered frocks, her hair is tightly permed. They banter in pet names: *Bloody-bitch, Silly-bugger, Stupid-git …*

The curate's house is flimsy, modern.
Really lovely, Rob says too loud. *Look at this garden.*
I stare at the six foot square of bushes and lawn.
What's that called? The thing with hedges. Toupee something?
Topiary, I hiss.
Right, I could get into that. Lot of potential this place.
What? I mouth.
Rob says louder, *It's got a lot of potential.*
Back at the vicarage his euphoria of pain relief wears off.
Deacon-wife commands me to go with her to the vestry.
Sod-fart over there can finish lunch. She gestures at Vicar-husband. *He's done fuck all else today,*
She tells me she hates the parish; that Vicar-husband accepted it without consulting her; that he gets paid, while she does all the work. *I told him—if we appoint a woman she'd better be married. I hope that's some guarantee.*
She doesn't wait for my reply, says, *I'll be your role model.*

Lunch ready, Bastard-features? She asks as we return.
All finished, Honey-bitch. Vicar-husband smiles.

My pastoral tutor tells me that the diocese has withdrawn that post. *Apparently there are problems in the marriage.* As I leave she clears her throat. *There was one other thing… They did say Rob didn't take much part. They found him rather off-putting. Please make sure it doesn't happen again.*

21

Smells—

A Tory and a Freemason. But Canon Pillsbury is keen to meet. He says shared faith is all we need. I'm six months pregnant, running out of options. I go alone. He has a packed weekend all planned: supper party, youth group, two services and lunch. He asks whether Rob is frustrated as a *house-husband* or simply *inadequate as a man.*
I've invited people for drinks, he says at ten that night.
I'm introduced as *the one doing a PhD in feminist theology.*
Contradiction in terms, dear girl, booms a red-faced man. *God's a man. Not that I have anything against you delightful girls.*
I sip my orange juice.
A woman, fiftyish, dyed blonde hair, Walt Disney lipstick, nudges Red-faced man. *Don't mind him. That curacy's got a lovely garden—you could run a lovely little toddler group there.*
And is your husband going to look after this baby too? A smartly dressed woman asks.
Bit weird isn't it? Red-faced man demands, his face shiny from whisky.
He's got no choice, I say, *I'm a feminist. I force him to stay at home.*
See! What did I tell you? Razor sharp or what? First class mind! Canon Pillsbury laughs, gulps whisky, winks at me.

8 a.m.: three elderly ladies and a cloud of incense attend the service—

22

and alarm bells

We march back to the Rectory for breakfast.
Help yourself. Butter's in the fridge.
I open a floor to ceiling fridge of alcohol.
No, the other fridge. That one belongs to my wife.
Only the cloud of incense and the tinkle of bells distinguish the 10 o'clock Communion as *high church*. The congregation responds in monotone. Afterwards I stand by the door to say good-bye.
Hi, I'm Stacey. Look, I realise you don't know me, but if I were you I wouldn't touch this place...
I wouldn't say this was a happy church... warns the next.
You know he's a Free Mason? They hold their services here. A lot of us object...
Last curate had a breakdown, says a thin, smart-suited man.

I'm delivered to the warden's house for lunch.
I'll come right out with this. Pillsbury's a bastard, past master at breaking curates, takes pleasure in it.
The church warden's wife sighs and nods.
Anyway, dear, you enjoy your lunch.

Canon Pillsbury sees me onto the train before phoning Rob to ask how he *really* feels about *all this role reversal malarkey*. He tells Rob not to mention the call to me.

And they remain two

The letter offering me the post says that my relationship to Canon Pillsbury should be thought of as a marriage— *with absolute clarity and none of this role reversal nonsense.* He encloses a torn out sheet from the parish news in which he's written that his decision to offer me the post: *could only be likened to offering it to a very effeminate gay male candidate, because of the perversity of Meg's lifestyle.*

My pastoral tutor tells me he has every right to his *models of ministry,* says I'm over-reacting, that I'm silly to decline this post; urges me to reconsider.

Reader, I don't marry him.

What are you doing here?

We drive in silence. The door bell plays an Easter hymn.
Gary wears an imitation leather jacket—bomber style. His
receding hair is long. His wife smiles all the time, serves
us chicken. *I forgot to mention you only eat rabbit food*, Gary
says. Deb smiles, scurries to the freezer.

Gary shows us round our prospective home. The fireplace
is torn out. There's an odour of mildew and urine. *Not bad,
eh?* Gary asks. *The parish will give you twenty quid a year to
do it up.*
It's 1988.
Half the congregation left last month, he adds. *They need to
learn humility. Do you want to see upstairs?*

After the Sunday service people huddle at the back of
church, sipping bitter drinks from plastic cups. Others
kneel at the front for 'a time of ministry'. Gary and two
acolytes lay hands on them to ward off Satan. A greasy-
haired young man begins to rock and moan. Next to him a
plump woman slumps to the floor.
Yes, Lord, yes, Lord. Yes, yes, yes! Gary chants.
A thin, grey man approaches Rob. *Haven't you read any
Scripture? Don't you know St. Paul commands the husband to
be the head of his household?*
Rob says, before he walks away, *I leave theological questions
to my wife.*

St. Valentine's Day. We drive home without a word. That
night we exchange identical cards. Snap! And we snap
and snarl at one another, tear the cards to shreds; fall
silent.

Crying out in the wilderness

The file contains the last remaining vacant post. I phone
the parish priest.
The thing is, Meg, we've had to call a halt. Finding a curate is
proving quite a strain. If you're still looking next year...
I see. I pause. *No, actually I don't. Do you know how few posts*
there are for women?
I understand, but ...
Do you?
Pardon?
Do you understand?
He listens to my whole tirade: the saga of every bigot I've
ever met. Then I say I'll send my C.V.
I end: *If you're like the rest, don't bother to reply.*
Two weeks later his letter arrives.

Dear Meg,
Your persistence and what you said mean I simply cannot
ignore...

A son given to us?

It's a boy? I ask. They've told me I am carrying a boy; saw it on the scan. I crane to see my second son across the screen that hides my gaping abdomen.
Yes, the doctor says, then: *Wait a minute. It's a girl.*
And Lauren—fierce and fragile—is here among us as from nowhere.

The caesarean scar is tender, two weeks old.
Breakfast? Rob asks.
No time. I'll have a Mars bar after worship—I'll be in need of comfort food by then.
Rob sighs, says, as always, *You shouldn't be going in. It's not as though you have any lectures.*
Spiritual formation, I reply
Bullshit!
No, but the nappy-changing wives leave plenty of baby shit.

I'm in solitary again.

No place for them in the curacy

Simon is on holiday when we move in. The warden drops
off keys and runs away. *Unbelievable*, Rob says, counting
strides across the room—five or six; maybe twelve in
length. *Unbelievable*.
I peer into a galley kitchen, *Is this it?*
Unless the garden doubles as a dining room.
Our furniture won't fit. We switch to a flat-pack life.

Dear Meg,
I must remind you that unless your loan is paid at once I
will be forced to let your bishop know. Those in debt
cannot be ordained.
With every blessing for your future ministry,
Colin †

The cheque was sent two days ago. I am redeemed.

Go therefore and make disciples…

New in post, I make a list of toddler groups to visit; the children and a dog-collar my dual calling cards.

I'm Meg. I've just moved in.

The slender woman glances at the plastic strip tucked into the collar of my clergy shirt.

New curate, I explain.

She nods. *Let me show you round.*

A dark-haired little girl, Mole's age, grabs the woman's skirt. I'm introduced to chatting mums, who try to hide their curiosity.

I'm Annie by the way, the woman says. *I don't think I've ever been inside a church.*

Another nods.

I've been meaning to get mine Christened, says a third.

That they might have life... abundantly

I prepare the altar in the quiet of the empty church. This is my favourite time: an oasis between leaving home and Communion, when anything might happen.
Rob arrives with Lauren and Mole—hair uncombed, pyjamas showing underneath his clothes. I cringe and Simon laughs.

The versicle, *The Lord be with you.*
Hello, Mummy, the response.

Mole makes a dash from the pew while Lauren starts to wail. Blotting out the *tutts* of the back row, I close my eyes and preach, 'That they may have life...'

Come and see

You must be Meg, a dark-eyed, smiling woman says. *I'm Elise. I've heard good things, so I thought I'd come and see.* She laughs, holds out her hand. *How Biblical is that?*
I can't say I've seen you under a fig, I reply.
Come to tea on Tuesday. We can swap stories about PhDs.
She finds a pew.

Simon prophesies that we'll have hordes of families, but only a trickle arrives. *Family Communions indeed*, the back row hiss. Simon preaches, undeterred, *This morning's Gospel tells us that children are the first in the kingdom. As a new father again...* The back row sucks in air. *I'm reminded that there is a child in all of us...*
Poppycock, someone in the back row jeers.
Lauren starts to cry. *Shh, shh*, Rob sooths, as Mole begins to bang a book against the pew.
Simon smiles and continues.

It's an absolute disgrace, back row number, praying mantis thin, proclaims, cornering Simon at the door. *Children running around, you blathering on about being a child.*
Unholy nonsense, number two, as round as Humpty Dumpty, but without his optimism, puts in. *We'll go elsewhere in future.*
Number one agrees, jutting out a bony mantis chin, *Somewhere with decency.*

Not call anyone… unclean

It must be hard, a white haired priest at chapter breakfast says, *I said a Mass for you. It's what I do—in the face of the immovable; I say a Mass.*

He's the only colleague to acknowledge the absence of my ordination to the priesthood—an Anglo-Catholic former monk. A year after college, Nick and Lewis, all my male peers, are being ordained.

I get a call from Delia Watts, BBC. It's a pale October day; the wind has blown me back from Morning Prayer.

I'm doing a documentary on the women left behind. We want to film a service in your church, show the viewers what women aren't allowed to do.

Simon's pause is palpable, but he finds *no* hard to say and feels the weight of guilt for the whole church.

Unable to speak

Simon, I've got some news. We're in his study. *I'm... going to have a baby.*

Simon pales. *I ... I think... will you excuse me?*

After Evening Prayer that day, and all that week, Simon scuttles away. The next week he's away on holiday.

Hi Meg. Simon smiles.

Good holiday?

Lovely. It's just when I get back...

You wonder what you are doing here. I finish for him. *It'll soon wear off.*

Meg, I'm sorry about before. I panicked. You will come back, after the baby I mean?

Of course I will, I reassure.

Do not worry about tomorrow

Mark Bannerman here, the phone voice says. *Diocesan Secretary. It's about the... er—maternity leave.*
I see. Is there a policy?
Well, er—no. A pause. *But it's happened once before. Before my time. I wonder—if I give you her number—could you find out what the arrangement was?*

Hello, Mark, Meg Tennison here. Julia had six months leave with pay, but told the bishop not to let anyone get away with that again!
Ah. He pauses. *Her husband's a barrister. Probably didn't need the money. Anyway, since we last spoke, the bishop's council had a talk—quite heated, I understand. So the bishop's decided to meet with your Archdeacon and myself to make a plan. I'll put in a good word.*

Two days later I receive a summons from Derek Dingleby, Archdeacon. We sit in his study, bigger than the whole of our downstairs. He talks of my *condition* in a whisper, makes a sudden speech about our inadequate house, for which, he insists, Simon is to blame.

Later Mark calls to say the bishop has agreed to pay full stipend for six months. *But it's not a policy,* he adds. *These things* are apparently better dealt with case by case.

Anointed

I've resigned. Rob throws his coat across a chair. *This Archdeacon told the parish that anything they owed the diocese would be taken out of my salary. They can find another ransom. I'd earn more stacking shelves.* Rob slumps beside his coat. *Sam has something coming up; maternity cover, but full time while it lasts.*

I hardly sleep the night before the birth. The morning is elastic as I wait for the caesarean. Finally she's here—my Rosa—like somebody I've always known, taking in the world through midnight eyes. I learn massage from a midwife who's been touring India; anointing Rosa in camomile and rose.

Foxes have holes

As unasked for as miracles, Derek Dingleby calls two months into my leave.
I'm ringing about your move, he says
Move? I rub my head, confused.
Your next post, Meg.
But I've still got eighteen months to go.
I wind my hand into a hank of hair.
I understand, but with the house being so unsuitable we thought it best to move you now. I've found the perfect place: two churches, rector, team vicar — they need a woman to complement the team. Interview's on Tuesday.

We go by bus, Rosa in her sling. The rector's forty-ish, tall with fine receding hair and eyes so pale they're almost colourless. Team vicar is a bulky man who heaves in breath. They don't tell me their names, but joke about my PhD, ask if I'm a *strident feminist.*
I used to be married to one of those, Short-breathed vicar says.
The Archdeacon should have said that we intend to advertise, Pale-eyed rector says. *I've no idea what makes him think we'll take the bishop's pet. You can apply like anyone else. You'd better attend services in the next few weeks.*
We visit the church in unseasonable April snow. Derek Dingleby urges me to see the house, insists that the interviews are *only for form.*
A letter arrives to say I haven't been short-listed: I possess too many qualifications and insufficient age. They can't give me a post *just because I need a house.*
The bishop writes to apologise for any *miscommunication.*

See how these Christians love one another

Two days later Dingleby finds another parish. This one is
a *challenge*, he says, warning me not to talk to the leaving
deacon. I phone her straight away.

There's an assistant priest, older than Methuselah, hates women,
Melanie begins. *The vicar has promised no woman will ever be
ordained priest here. And that's not all. I had twins last year,
total shock. The parish council decided I couldn't return to work
full time. No consultation. The bishop agreed. Part time in this
place means forty hours a week for less than five thousand a
year. My husband had given up work to look after the twins.
You can imagine how it's been. He's got a new job. I don't mind
if I never see inside a church again.*

Oh, Melanie, I say.

*Don't come here, Meg. Oh, by the way, the house is full of
damp. Don't come here.*

Meg, I must urge you to go and see St. Barth's, Derek
Dingleby insists. *I should warn you that there is unlikely to be
another post for you in this diocese. We can't go on making offer
after offer for you to turn down.*

Women in waiting

We meet on the steps of St Martin's. Rosa sleeps in her sling. Rob shepherds Lauren and Mole. Next to me women shoulder the banner high for the press to see, the letters in lime on a mustard cloth. Others brandish placards. We sing and sway in solidarity; process to Westminster Abbey ten by ten, outwitting restrictions on Whitehall marches—become an unbroken line as we reach the doors.

In the newspapers an opponent warns the world to be on guard—we may talk in the language of prayer, he says, but women's ordination is ungodly, secular. The priesthood is no battleground for women's liberation or New Age gibberish about the feminine side of God. Tradition is not a toy. These women will split the church in two.

Not without honour except...

I wake up tired and thirty. My stomach sags: elephant flesh from three caesarean wounds. My breasts still leak. My post remains in limbo. Rob manages an unwrapped gift; no cards from the children.

Midsummer's day I cross Waterloo Bridge, leave Rosa for a whole hour while I viva my PhD, return home to pace beside the phone. It rings at last. Elated I phone Simon with the news. *Ah, right,* he says. Then: *not that it makes any difference, of course. You won't mind if I don't repaint the notice board; no point flaunting something no-one cares about.*

At our next meeting I have a plan: *When I leave you'll be looking for someone experienced,* I say. *So why don't I stay?*
Simon falters. *I don't understand.*
This place is growing, there's plenty of work. I could stay.
But the house...
We're used to the house.
I'm not sure... Simon's voice is tight. He talks too fast. *It's a big transition.* He attempts a laugh. *You know how competent women scare me, Meg.* He slumps in his seat. *I wasn't expecting this,* he says, looking hurt.
I nod, flash him an indulgent smile.
We should look at arrangements for your return to work. He steadies his voice. *I need your assurance that child care is in place, that we'll still get your best work. We should advertise your post by the New Year. I realise it runs till autumn, but there's no need to draw it out.*
I only nod.

House on sand

I return to work and the search for a post. One priest wants to share with me his ministry: the iron hand concealed in a kid glove, another wants to interview Rob. I arrive back in the diocese we left three years ago. A council estate. An all women short-list for a post beneath the attention of any man. The rector is affable: neat white hair, sharp blue eyes, aging suits, clerical shirts in grey: a Low Church badge. The daughter church, my church, Chris describes as *a brave little place*. The walls are damp, set with tell-tales to measure their movement.

A *mere precaution*, Chris says, *simply to check it's settled.*

And great was its fall

An uneasy winter. Simon is tense. Rob is anxious about the move and finding work. I juggle child care, prepare to leave my friends, and the children's friends, behind. One frost-crisp morning, waving Rob off to work from an upstairs window, Rosa against my shoulder, Lauren and Mole waiting for their day, I lean into the window pane. Shards glint in Rob's car mirror as he drives away. My mind is empty of everything but blood—and a far off sound of shattering glass.

Rob is in the room. Children are crying. Rob doesn't speak, not even to say, *there are no accidents.*

After the stitches he drives us home.
Silent, he leaves for work.

Laughter be turned into mourning

The photo in a glossy women's magazine shows a laughing young mum. On my lap, Lauren is serious and calm, Rosa, plump and giggling. Mole sits next to us. The children are brightly dressed. I wear a clerical shirt in cobalt blue. On the page a quote from Rob:

> *IT'S BEEN DIFFICULT TO WATCH MEG BEING HURT BY NOT BEING ORDAINED. THE INJUSTICE ANGERS ME.*

This is Meg's last service Simon says.
Elise leads the circle in prayer. Candles are lit to signify our thanks and sorrow. Simon places his candle first. *I want to say thank you for Meg,* he says, *and offer my sorrow that she has to go.* He pauses. *My regret…* He dips his head: *…things could have been different, but I lost the moment…* He glances at me. I close my eyes. *…and now she's leaving.*

At my leaving party Simon raises a toast to three things: my work with children, my magenta duffle coat—a sign, he says, of how much the church has changed—and my constant smile.

And joy into dejection

The vicarage, in fake Cotswold stone, is out of place on the grey estate. The parish administrator arrives to help. *Hello there.* George grins at Mole. He has black curls, a lilting voice. *What d'you call a blind deer?* Mole blinks at George. *No eye-deer,* George says and laughs. Mole slowly gets the idea and nods.

George helps us unpack and decorate, put up curtains and shelves, stick plastic glow-in-the-dark stars to the bedroom ceilings.

We share the house with builders who smoke in my study, leave power tools plugged in for children to find, prop the front door open to the road. We comfort ourselves—soon they will be gone, all this space will be ours, even a garden—a garden of clay that buckles spade after spade; a garden into which passers-by fling bottles and trash, used syringes; a garden where only brambles grow. The local children scale the fence to scavenge for toys.

It's two months before the builders leave.

They return often—to repair the boiler again and again and—the windows leak—and the kitchen blooms dry rot—and the bath is pitted with forty years of stains—and the windowsills hail concrete gobs—

I should warn visitors to take care at the door, the diocesan surveyor says.

I could put up a sign, I say. *This Vicarage is a hard hat area.*

I don't think that's funny, he says.

Nor do I, I agree and put down the phone.

Have mercy on us

The church is built on a raft over clay. The raft has long since cracked. The walls are moving away. Damp and fungus decorate the interior and the air is sweet with rotten scent. The congregation, a remnant, have traded hope for blame. There is no Sunday school. Someone explains that the church banned the children of a previous vicar; unanimously. The children were well behaved, but no-one liked the hymns he chose or the vicar's wife. When he left, their parting gift was a tankard inscribed: *We don't do that here.* Chris is unabashed. *They're ready to be rebuilt from the heart,* he says. On Sundays women kneel at the altar rail, and refuse the wine from my hands. Women, they fear, taint blood. *It makes my blood boil!* Rob rails, preparing Sunday lunch. Mole sits at the table, colouring in the Lamb of God who takes away the sins of the world.

Star at its rising

1992, July: Again we're told, *not yet*. We remain women in waiting. Rob can't find work. The parish team's an uneasy mix of grating souls.

Remembrance Day. I stand outside Church House. Westminster drizzle seals in cold. The speeches are made. I hear how the church, like a village oak, stands trembling under an axe. I am that axe: me and all the would-be women priests.

In the early dark, I walk towards a TV crew—an interview I've agreed—and a man looms across my path, tall and cloaked. *You witch!* he shouts. *Do you hear me, witch? You are a witch!* I don't reply to my brother in Christ.

I'm doing the maths as the vote comes in. *YES!* the BBC reporter cheers. *Not that I'm taking sides.*

On camera I say, *It's how we see God: inclusive, God with us, fully human.* I hug my magenta duffel coat against the rain. A cheer erupts. A firework blazes across the sky like a single star:

Epiphany.

How long, O Lord?

Will you be a priest on Sunday, Mummy? Asks Mole.
No, but soon, I say.

Church to get vicars in knickers, runs one head-line.
Turmoil over Synod Vote, the *Telegraph*.
Steady As You Go, The Church Tells Women.

Rejoicing, we're told, is distasteful and insensitive. We're
told to wait. These things cannot be rushed. There's
protocol. Means must be found to soothe those hurt by us.
Grey winter turns to still-grey spring. I preach to a
congregation of five, take funerals, run community
groups... *Forward in Faith* threatens to cripple the church
with schism and compensation claims. Synod offers
safeguards against our taint, but the opposition presses for
more.

October 1993: Parliament votes 215 to 21 for women
priests.

November 1993: *The Act of Synod* passes—those unable to
countenance women priests will function separately,
accountable to bishops untainted by ordaining women.
The name for this is *two integrities*. In the synod gallery a
group of women unfurl a banner:
Shame.

Fruitful and multiply

New Year 1994:
I tell Chris first, *I'm expecting another baby.*
He's jubilant and so is George. Jeremy is not so pleased. *So you'll be taking maternity leave?* the curate asks. *You realise this has implications for me? And you'll be pregnant when you're ordained? I'm not comfortable with that.*

False prophets will arise

I'm summoned to the Bishop's Palace. The room where, seven years ago, he offered me a loan. In less than twenty minutes he's *tested* my vocation: I will be ordained.

The local headline reads: *Deacon Blazing a Trail for Women Priests.* The article is positive, though the journalist can't help but note how brave I am to work in such a place. The *Daily Mail* warns of exodus. The *Telegraph* misattributes quotes to me: that I can't help feeling triumphalist; that I joke about singing 'Onward Christian Soldiers' at the ordination service. The journalist can't help but wonder if we are driving away the church's most talented people: men.

Bringing you good news?

Crusaders for Women Priests Set New Firsts, says the *Guardian*, February 19th 1994. I'm described as a pregnant deacon on a long crusade. *Time* magazine's article, *Romeward Bound*, pictures me inside the church while a young male cleric stands outside, forlorn; my ordination a feminist battle to split the church.

Meg's Nappy Event No.4 Will Make History, says *The Western Daily Press*. I'm pictured, smiling, beside three serious children. The same picture appears in the *Daily Mail*, in black and white, with the prophecy: *Exodus from Church may cost £100 million*. My maternity leave is, I read, unprecedented: *Enough to induce cardiac arrest*, says one report. Sympathetic, *Deutsche Welle* come to stay, next *BBC World Service, Figaro...* The French ask me to iron vestments for a photograph. *No housekeeper?* marvels a sleek journalist from Argentina. *You do your own cooking? A priest?* I turn down a late-night live debate. They offer bribes: expensive hotel, a helicopter ride. *But my director wants the pregnant one*, the assistant wails. When we refuse to have photographers at the birth, an editor from a national tabloid paper phones and offers money—first to charity, then to us. *We always get our story*, he growls. We switch to a hospital forty miles away. Another reporter proposes to write a book—fly-on-the-wall, says he'll move in—just for three months; we'll forget he's there. He tells me the Foreign Legion tried to turn him down, but he got his way.

Not this time.

Your people shall be my people

The March sky is the thinnest blue. The cathedral is crammed with extra chairs; cameras and lights are scaffolded around the pillars. The rehearsal is interminable. Three rows of seats, thirty-two in all, set out near the altar.

Do we have to kneel for all of this? One woman asks.

Yes, Bishop Colin's voice is tense.

What about Meg?

What about Meg? The bishop casts me a weary glance.

I'm fine, I confirm.

She's fine. Meg's fine! the bishop reiterates. *Can we get on?*

The third run-through is smooth.

The media are let in to jostle for positions at the photo shoot.

Are we ready? Bishop Colin twists to survey our cassocked rows. *Sit up, Meg!*

The woman next to me says, *She's sitting up, Bishop, that's…*

I know what it is, thank you!

She grins and asks: *Will you be ordaining Meg's baby, Bishop?*

Don't be ridiculous! You know ordination can't cross the placental barrier.

He's serious.

The cameras flash. *This way, please! If you could turn towards me!* Then interviews. *I've found the pregnant one!* a young photographer shouts, attracting a crowd.

At the retreat house, Bishop Colin tells us to forget the past; exclusion has shaped us so far, but now we belong: it's time to forget injustices.

Firm in your faith…

Twenty-eight weeks pregnant. Expectation clogs the air. Women iron vestments, help each with hair clips and nail polish. In the chapel stained glass scatters colours across the bleached wood floor. Thick cream candles burn either side of a pale wood altar. Thirty-two women bring a chant to its close. And Bishop Colin stands to deliver his charge.

We might feel that this is once more into the breach, but it is not so: the battle is over and this is not the eve of St. Crispin's day. No, now is the time to give thanks and sing. Now is the time to stand fast and be faithful. For at the last, this is all that is asked: that we keep the faith.

The church of Philadelphia sends greetings

The cathedral entrance is lined with journalists. In the cloister room, set aside for robing, a telegram arrives addressed to me—

To our reverend sisters as you begin your priestly ministries. Grace to you, and peace. Joy and courage. From your 60 sister clergy in Philadelphia.

There is a moment of reverence as we remember these women, ordained in an 'illegal' ceremony to force the hand of the Episcopalian church.

On a table lie thirty-two long stemmed red roses: a gift from a Roman Catholic father of five girls.

Veni Sancti Spiritus

The plump Provost claps his hands. The words of the processional hymn reverberate as we wind into the aisle. *Praise to the Lord, the Almighty...* We are robed in white, embroidered stoles worn like the sashes of beauty queens for the last time. Cameras flash. The service is a blur of music, lights and liturgy. At the moment of ordination we stand in an arc. *Is it therefore your will that they should be ordained priests?*
It is! The assent is as loud as Apocalypse. No one objects. We go forward one by one.
Send down the Holy Spirit upon your servant Meg...

At the exchange of Peace a standing ovation booms; the congregation erupting in euphoria of greeting. I see Lauren in her cream silk dress, fair hair escaping in wisps from a dark blue ribbon. Six years old and confident, she shakes hands with everyone in her path. *That new priest is my mummy*, she tells each one. Cameras flash like the birth of a universe.

A message by a fool

Letters arrive from around the world—congratulations from Mo Mowlam, M.P. from the town where I grew up, from friends and strangers around the world; even an elderly man in Malaysia, whose letter begins, *Praise to the Lord...*

The newspapers divide. The *Times* notes profound anxiety at the destruction of English culture. The *Sunday Times* features a bill board proclaiming the murder of the Church of England. The *Observer* compares the ordination to the Reformation: a revolution.

Mothering Sunday, March 13th 1994: I celebrate Communion for the first time. Lent is suspended. For once St. Edmund's is full—of daffodils and people. Simon arrives from London, fusses over my chasuble, smoothing it like a parent at his only daughter's graduation. He tells me the world is different today. Not least because half the clergy in his Deanery will no longer speak to him after he's preached here.

Ces Femmes Qui Font Pleurer Le Pape, reads the headline in the *Paris Match.* A two page spread pictures the women who caused the Pope to cry.

Let her glean

There is no diocesan policy on maternity leave. I'm called to the Archdeacon's house. Humphrey Wainscot is shocked to hear that my last diocese gave six months paid leave: shocked. Surely I can return to work six weeks after a caesarean, but even this is far too generous. He'll do his best to negotiate six weeks, but it's a lot to ask; he can't make promises. The letter arrives on the day that we're burgled (again) and the car breaks down (again). It points out I am not employed and not entitled to any maternity leave. But, in spite of this, the diocese will be generous and allow me six weeks, four to be taken before the birth.

Rob repeats and repeats, *What do they mean you're not employed?* Then switches to, *So how come you pay tax?* And, *So why do you work sixty hours a week?*

I cut into Rob's litany. *Do you know I can take eight weeks sick leave without a doctor's note? Will I be well enough to work two weeks after a caesarean?*

He shakes his head.

I've got this year's holiday and Chris will swap at least two weeks leave from before the birth to afterwards to cover him for summer festivals.

I can see you've thought this through, Rob says.

Not a good report

The reporter on the phone says he got my number from
the diocese; that my *employers* expect my full co-operation.
He wants to cover the birth of a baby to one of the first
women priests, including photographs.
No.
But your employers said…
I doubt it, I say, *I'm not even employed.*
He switches to bribes.
We could come to an arrangement, Mrs Tennison.
Dr, it's Dr Tennison. Which nationals do you supply?
He's flustered. I haven't forgotten the tabloid editor's
threat, *We always get our story…*
Not this one.

Poured out like water

In hospital I spend a sleepless night; the last night that I will carry another life inside. Silas emerges sticky with newness, but no sign of ontological change. Three days later I'm back at home, the caesarean wound aching from forty miles in the car, my breasts engorged. The house is full of balloons. I sit under a banner, made by Rosa, Lauren and Mole, to welcome Silas home and am besieged by hormones: desolation and euphoria.

Who would do this?

Colleagues phone to unburden their mutual stress. There's a call to ask me to apply for grants to save the church from falling down. *Don't try to stay in this parish too long,* Humphrey Wainscot told me three years ago. *It will always be Good Friday here.* The garden is burgled while I'm asleep with Silas, one week old. Rob is out with the children. Lauren's slide has slid across a six foot fence. Three months, three burglaries. Mole notices a church on TV and is astonished to see it full of people. I ring Humphrey Wainscot who says he'll sound out opportunities. Summer turns to autumn. It's late November when he returns the call. I'm alone. Silas is fretful and I struggle to hold the phone. Wainscot's tone is strained and formal, the words too fast, *No vacant parishes... for the foreseeable future...* I know of two vacancies and two retirements coming up. *...a particular strain on jobs for women... look to your own future... we're willing to release you.*

I'm back eight years.
Silas begins to wail.

Always Good Friday

My first day back: four people in Church and the stink of damp clings to the altar cloth. The walls have a fresh coat of mould. As I lift the chalice I think of Jesus taking the bread, giving thanks, knowing he's already betrayed. Thanks in the face of betrayal, without the hindsight of resurrection.

It will always be Good Friday here.

Who can stand before his cold?

The interviews begin again. St. Bede's is a south coast clone of St. Edmund's, desperate enough to take a woman priest. My half of the parish is beyond the canal, *a bit of a challenge*. High-rise flats surround the church. There's a burnt out car by the door. Inside: the smell of abandonment. Out-of-date notices sag with dust. *It's a small congregation,* the rector says, *not sure how they'll take to a woman, but they love the Lord.* The house is beside a railway line. The garden: mud bordered by razor wire. The rooms are dark and wallpaper peels in a damp display of history. *Needs a lick of paint.* Every room has holes gouged into the walls. *Radiators,* the rector says. *Last chap took them away.*

Who hopes for what is seen?

After the next interview the local Archdeacon, Paul Kent, rings to say that I was that the only choice, but he can't offer me the post—Kevin and Darren, church warden and vicar of the sister church, feel there's something wrong; they suspect I'm far too competent. *So I'm being turned down because I'm the best candidate?* He says he will get back to me. The bishop steps in and interviews me. I hear nothing for a week and phone Paul Kent again. The bishop wants to appoint me. Darren is holding out.

While the wrangling goes on I travel to an interview in Sheffield: shiny new building, executive suburbs. They tell me how much the Lord has provided; they pray and money rolls in. The Rural Dean pulls on his beard. *I couldn't help over-hearing you have a child. I have to say, I wouldn't have interviewed you if I'd known.*

Paul Kent reconvenes the interview. Kevin says he's having a bad day, turns his back and doesn't talk again. Whenever I speak Darren looks the other way. Two hours later I'm left in a waiting room. Another hour and the suffragen bishop leaves. Another hour and I'm dismissed. A week goes by. I phone Darren, who refuses to meet, says it's not his fault, there's something about me... *God bless,* he says and hangs up. I write to him. The reply, a week later, says the post-mark on my letter sent him into shock. There's still no change, but he wishes me well—*in Jesus.* Paul Kent offers another interview: another parish where no man is willing to work.
The congregation lives in hope.

Hope does not disappoint

Two years and I hardly stop to sleep. I fundraise to renew the hall, extend the church's community work. I work with schools and children's groups, run a counselling course. There are midweek services, choir practice, funerals, baptisms and weddings...
I hardly stop to sleep. I love my work.

In the first week the children's bikes are stolen. But someone offers old bikes in their place. Two weeks later the car is broken into, the children's coats are taken. But someone brings a bag of grown-out-of coats. Monthly, the windows are smashed. But they mend and now there's toughened glass. The children can't play in the garden—kids from the low-rise sit along the ten foot wall—throwing stones. The front door is marked from a crow bar attempt. One day the back door is lifted off its hinges. I watch it go.
I love my work.

The congregation lives in hope and so do I.

Stir up Sunday

It's the morning after the autumn fair. I sit alone on the vestry floor by the door of the open, empty safe. It is cold here in November, cold enough for a Christmas turkey store, I joke each week with the sacristan. It takes a long time to notice the cold today. I don't know how long I've sat like this: iced numb. I force myself to walk through the church, forgetting to lock each door on the way. As I reach the porch there's a rattling noise, someone banging the double door. I hear a thin whine become a wail. It's coming from me.

Meg! Meg! Rob hammers the door.

I slump on the other side and sob. Eventually I let him in.

The money... the fair... the... someone... the safe...

The police seem to appear immediately: a fair woman taking down details. I have it clear like a film, but the sound-track is gone, except for threats and expletives.

A step between me and death

I am leaving the church.
Are you the vicar?
Yes, can I help?
He pulls out a knife, pushes me back towards the church
and makes me lock us inside. He wants the safe. He is
medium height. Slim, not thin. Very pale, a sickly pale...
Drugs, the policewoman nods to herself.
Blue eyes. Black woollen hat. Ordinary jeans and trainers.
Black jacket, short with elastic waist. Sports bag, black.
And the knife?
Black handle. Thin blade. Maybe six inches. He waves it
close to my face. We walk down the aisle. He stays on my
left. He's agitated. I open the doors, kneel to open the safe.
The money's in canvas bags... from the fair, this
morning's collection, eight hundred, perhaps a thousand
pounds. Mostly loose change. The bags are heavy. There's
a door at the back of the church that leads to the field. I cut
my hand on the bolt. He pushes past. I slam the door and
throw the bolt and turn the key. I sit by the safe. I don't
know how long.

Miserable comforters

Rob leaves a message on Paul Kent's phone. The doorbell and telephone ring all day. Early Monday, Paul Kent arrives anxious and tired. At the press conference rows of flash guns spark and the journalists ask if a woman should work in a parish like this. I tell them it's safer for me than a man, that perhaps I'm less threatening to a young man on drugs.

And Paul Kent smiles.

When they ask how much money, D.I. Bevin cuts in. *We just want to say, a substantial amount.*

Do you have a message for him?

I say the right things: *compassion, forgiveness.*

And Paul Kent smiles and nods; tells them that the diocese takes security seriously, but they must understand that our work demands a level of vulnerability.

Bishop Eliot phones. *Meg, I just heard. You've been in touch with Paul Kent?* His voice is terse.

Yes, Rob phoned straight away. The Archdeacon was here for the press conference.

Good. It's important to handle the media well. The bishop hangs up.

The days are full of photo-fits and police updates. Someone cashes three canvass bags at the local bank: correct description. A man in the queue calls it in, but the cameras at the bank are switched off.

But find no rest

I love my work and now I can't stop. I sleep less and less and I do the washing at 2 a.m.—it gives me more time for work. I must keep busy. The more Rob begs, *slow down*, the faster I go. I don't take my post-Easter break. Rob asks Paul Kent for help, but the Archdeacon says it's none of his business if I want to work and in any case I'm getting results and I seem okay to him.

When I grow up, I don't want to be a priest, offers six-year-old Rosa at dinner one night. *You never get to see your children and bad men might kill you.*

It's seven months before I take a holiday.
I go to bed. It's only an ache at first. My body feels heavy. My eyes are sore. My throat is raw. I have abdominal pains. Even in bed I feel afraid, a bleak foreboding… or rage. I cry and cry and I long for darkness. It's July outside, but I'm icy cold. I crave only sleep, but I find no rest.

Whitewash with lies

At home, Rob phones Paul Kent. *No, she's in bed... No, she can't arrange service cover herself... She's seeing the G.P. tomorrow... But she doesn't need a sick note for eight weeks... The Church Commissioners' guidelines say so, but she'll get one anyway... Yes, she really is ill...*

I sleep for a month, but I'm never refreshed. The children become solicitous.

Alex Derwent, the Rural Dean, insists he must see me alone; diocesan patience is wearing thin. *You must understand that hiding away starts rumours... you never answer the phone or the door. It's easy to see how people might think that there's something strange going on... It's only natural they'll think that it's Rob who is... We're simply concerned... and you know you can tell me if Rob ever... We can't see why else you'd take to your bed...*

I see a consultant for breast pain and lumps. I see a consultant for abdominal pain. My body—in shock— floods with hormones. My GP says we should also consider...

The diocesan women's officer visits; tells Rob she must see me alone. She hints that my stipend will soon be cut off.

At Christmas I force myself back to work.

I dread my work.

Resurrection

Easter Sunday. I notice him enter the church. He's thin, unshaven, constantly glances over his shoulder, asks to speak to the lady vicar. He watches Fred, the church warden, walk away.

He's one of them, he whispers, nodding at Fred's retreating Sunday suit. *We haven't got much time.*

He takes my arm. *They've got my daughter. They've infected her brain. God said you would understand.*

Winnie appears, watering can in hand.

You get away! He shouts. I know you! Winnie edges away.

I have to take you to God, he hisses.

Fred and others appear, walking slowly down the aisles.

Don't come near! I know you. I know you all.

He clutches me tightly. Rob appears.

Keep away! He locks an arm around my neck.

Don't worry, he whispers. *We'll both go to God.*

Someone suggests making a grab, but Rob says no.

Let Meg talk, she's keeping him calm.

I realise I've been talking all the time.

The police appear, walk slowly down the aisles.

At the deanery service Paul Kent asks how I am. I mention the man. He cuts me off and shrugs. *That was nothing, nothing at all. You're looking well.*

Alex Derwent rolls his eyes. *Surely, you're not still bringing that up?*

A time to weep

My health declines in increments. I have mastitis every month. The abdominal pains increase. The church council agrees someone will always be here to open the church with me, but Tuesday comes—mid-week Communion—and I'm alone again. I lock myself in, knowing I'll have to open the doors before the service begins. As I reach the vestry a boy rushes in. *Where's the money? The fucking money!* He pushes past, grabs a jar of coins. *Pissing dump!* He throws the jar across the room. *Sod all fucking here!* He pushes me hard into the debris and runs. A two-foot shard sits less than an inch from my hand. My palm is flecked with fragments of glass, embedded like cactus hairs. I cross the room and lock myself in. I sit on the floor and weep and rock and rock and weep.

Hello! Meg! Are you alright? It's Kim from Guides. When I stand the pain in my shoulder makes me retch.
When the police have gone, Rob phones Paul Kent.
Of course I phoned the police... I realise they sell stories to the newspapers, but they still have to know... Well if the diocese doesn't want bad press it should do something... Yes, it was serious enough to report...
Rob puts down the phone. *Pompous prick.*

Hallelujah

For two weeks the pain in my arm grows worse till I wake unable to move, except when spasms hit. I sit in a neck brace, fogged with morphine. I hardly move for three weeks.

Alex Derwent brings flowers while Rob and the children are out; hand-picked, newspaper wrapped and wilting. He doesn't sit down. He paces the room lecturing me on how important it is that I should be seen to cope—I must not give in to the ups and downs of life. I should get back to work and not make too much of this; think of my future. Where is my faith?

I go back to work.

I have physiotherapy every week for a year before the physiotherapist admits defeat. Another consultant to see. I don't take days off. I hide the pain. I begin each day by throwing up. Sundays, I arrive early at church and vomit while I'm alone. There are those who see that all is not well: some are anxious, some—enraged—insist that I'm faking, that assaults can't cause... that if anything's wrong it must be domestic, it must be Rob... I make a statement to the PCC. The angry become incensed.

Broke it

I am held at knife point and they parade it to raise church funds, I am overcome with grief and they turn from me, I am sick and they whisper that my husband must be beating me, I am held hostage and they silence me, I am thrown into broken glass and they sneer at me, I am weak and they are disgusted with me.

When I am in pain, they do not offer to pray with me and I wonder where the faith is. When I am in shock, they do not talk of God and I wonder where the hope is. When I begin to break, they do not offer bread and wine and I wonder where the love is.

In remembrance of…

All Soul's Day, November 2001. The bereaved arrive to remember those they loved. The names are read and, one by one, candles are lit and, on the white altar, a red carnation laid down for each name. In remembrance of…
Outside, the November air is as sharp as glass.
Winnie says she won't forget this service: *the most moving All Soul's of my life.*
I shiver, look back at the church. Inside, candles burn on darkened sills and red carnations wilt in remembrance and I won't forget this service or ever step inside this church again.

Afterword

Stale Bread & Miracles is a novelised series of prose poems (or microfictions) and, as such, it is a work of fiction, despite the fact that at its core is a body of life writing drawing on journals kept over many years.

The events on which this sequence is based began with an interview in September 1985, when my vocation to become an ordained minister in the Anglican Church was tested. In September 1988 I was ordained deacon after a training period that stirred up more than its fair share of controversy because my first two children were born during my time at theological college. In March 1994 I was ordained priest at the first ever service of ordination of women to the priesthood in the Church of England. At the time I was pregnant with my fourth child. In the two weeks leading up to the ordination I took part in over fifty interviews for media outlets around the globe. The service was recorded by the world's media as a moment in history. It was the culmination of a vocation I'd felt strongly since I was twelve years old. I believed absolutely that God was in that moment and that the world was forever changed by it. Eight years later, after a series of assaults, I retired from ministry due to ill health. The deeper malaise, however, came not from random attacks by desperate people, but from the growing feeling that the church, as an institution, offered stale bread in place of communion. But there were also miracles: those who simply kept faith with their humanity.

Jan Fortune-Wood
August, 2008

Notes

Many of the titles are quoted from or are allusions to Biblical verses: Isaiah 43:1; Isaiah 44:3; Genesis 34:30; Matthew 6:34; Exodus 30:15; Numbers 22:32; Matthew 19:14; Acts 15: 20; Matthew 4:1; Hosea 1:9; Genesis 2:24; 1 Kings 19:9; John 1:23; Isaiah 9:6; Luke 2:7; Matthew 28:19; John 10:10; John 1:46; Acts 10:28; Luke 1:22; Matthew 6:34; Luke 9:58; Matthew 13:57; Matthew 7:26; Matthew 7:27; James 4:9; Matthew 2:2; Psalm 13:1; Genesis 1:28; Matthew 24:11; Luke 2:10; Ruth 1:16; 1 Corinthians 16:13; 1 Corinthians 16:19; Proverbs 26:6; Ruth 2:15; 1 Samuel 2:24; Psalm 22:14; Luke 22:23; Psalm 147:17; Romans 8:24; Romans 5:5; 1 Samuel 20:3; Job 16:2; Psalm 22:2; Job 13:4; Corinthians 11:24; Matthew 25:40-43; Ecclesiastes 3:4.

The phrase 'See how these Christians love one another' is based on a misquotation of Tertullian, *Apologeticum*, Chapter. 39, 7

'Have mercy on us' is a translation of *Kyrie Eleison* (Lord, have mercy), in turn a translation of a liturgical form going back to 10th or 11th century Czech liturgy.

'Once more into the breach...' William Shakespeare, *Henry V*: Act 3, Scene 1 and the reference to the eve of St. Crispin's day from Act 4, Scene 3.

Veni Sancti Spiritus – Latin – Come, Holy Spirit.

Headlines quoted on p.50 are from November 1992. On p.52, *'Deacon blazing...'* headline is from the *Evening Advertiser* 07.01.94; the *Daily Mail* headline is from 23.02.94. and allusions to the *Telegraph* are from 16.01.94. Headlines on p.53 are taken from the *Guardian* 19.02.94, *Time* Magazine 21.02.94, *Western Daily Press* 22.02.94 & the *Daily Mail* 23.02.94. On p.58 *'Ces Femmes Qui Font Pleurer Le* Pape' was the headline in the *Paris Match* 13.03.94.

Jan Fortune-Wood's previous books include three novels, *A Good Life* (Bluechrome Publishing, 2005); *Dear Ceridwen* (Cinnamon Press, 2007); *The Standing Ground* (Cinnamon Press, 2007) and a collection of poetry, *Particles of Life* (Bluechrome Publishing, 2005). She has also written widely on alternative education and parenting, her most recent book being *Winning Parent, Winning Child* (Cinnamon, 2005). She lives in North Wales with her husband and children and is currently learning Welsh.